FARNBOROUGH'S CATERPILLARS

An account of research flying and parachute escapes at the Royal Aircraft Establishment

by
Richard Dennis

Foreword by
Captain E M Brown, CBE, DSC, AFC, RN

Published by
Footmark Publications, Fleet, Hampshire

First published 1996

ISBN 0 9515738 8 8

Published by Footmark Publications,
12 The Bourne,
Fleet,
Hampshire GU13 9TL

Printed by Holmes & Sons (Printers),
10 High Street,
Andover,
Hampshire SP10 1NY

The front cover shows Lt Cdr Eric 'Winkle' Brown escaping from Tempest JN 735 on 26 July 1944, by well-known local artist Terry Harrison.

CONTENTS

Frontispiece: The exclusive Caterpillar gold pin (via Irvin Aerospace).

LIST OF ILLUSTRATIONS

FOREWORD

by
Captain E M Brown, CBE, DSC, AFC, RN
Chief Naval Test Pilot at RAE Farnborough 1944-49
CO Aerodynamics Flight, 1947-49

Research test flying is by its very nature a high risk business. The test crews involved are well aware of the risks, but rely on scientific prediction coupled with their own skills to reduce these. If all else fails, there is the last resort comfort of the parachute, which with the aid of some luck and a cool head will save the day.

The Royal Aircraft Establishment, Farnborough, was Britain's centre of aviation research for over 70 years, and inevitably there was a considerable price to pay in human lives for its test flying activities. However, this factual account of Farnborough's tally of parachute escapes not only captures the excitement of what went on there, but puts into perspective that the odds were not irrevocably stacked against the test crews.

As a test pilot at RAE for six years, I had reason to be thankful for the dedicated work of the Parachute Section, which was eventually headed up by Richard Dennis, and so he writes with particularly apt knowledge of his subject.

Like myself, the author is concerned to preserve the Farnborough wind tunnels as a reminder to the nation of the tremendous contribution the RAE made to the progress of aviation, and this book is dedicated to that goal.

Capt E M Brown, RN (sitting on the nose of a Spitfire) with fellow Aerodynamics Flight pilots at Farnborough, May 1944. Left to right: Sqdn Ldr A F Martindale, Sqdn Ldr J C Nelson, Lt Cmdr E M Brown, Sqdn Ldr D Weightman (ranks as in 1944). Three of these pilots feature in research flights described in 'Farnborough's Caterpillars'.

INTRODUCTION

Most people in the United Kingdom will have heard of the Farnborough Air Show, but the history of the airfield on which the show has been held for many years is not so well known.

Farnborough airfield can justifiably claim to be the birthplace of British Aviation, for it was here, on what was Farnborough Common in 1908, that S F Cody made the first officially recognised powered aeroplane flight in the United Kingdom. The Common later became the airfield of the Royal Aircraft Factory and then that of its successor, the Royal Aircraft Establishment (RAE 1918-1988), whose many contributions to the progress of aviation ranged from research into the design of fighter and bomber aircraft and the axial flow jet engine of World War 2, to Concorde, the first supersonic airliner to enter regular service.

In 1988 to reflect more accurately its changing research activities, the Establishment was renamed the Royal Aerospace Establishment. This proud title was lost early in 1991, when it became part of the business orientated Defence Research Agency (DRA), an Executive Agency of the Ministry of Defence. Later in 1991, the DRA declared the airfield to be "surplus to requirements" and in March 1994 all research flying was transferred to the Ministry of Defence airfield at Boscombe Down, Wiltshire.

Faced with the unthinkable, Farnborough airfield without research aircraft, the author, who joined the RAE as an apprentice in 1942 compiled a record of all the emergency escapes by parachute made by RAE test pilots and scientist/test observers during flights from Farnborough. Such aviators are entitled to become members of the renowned Caterpillar Club, whose sole entry qualification is to have saved one's life by parachute. Club members can wear, as a lapel pin, a small gold caterpillar, a reminder that early parachute fabrics were made of silk, obtained from the cocoon of the silk-worm caterpillar.

The stories behind the parachute escapes provide a timely account of some of the research flying from Farnborough airfield and serve as a tribute to the dedication and courage of the aircrew engaged in this vital research work. In describing the escapes in detail, the opportunity has also been taken to outline some of the scientific work in the laboratories of the Establishment associated with that in the air.

FIRST FLIGHTS AT FARNBOROUGH

Research flying started at Farnborough on 16 October 1908, the day that S F Cody made the first powered aeroplane flight in the United Kingdom. He took off from an open area on the eastern edge of Farnborough Common, a short distance from the site of the Army Balloon Factory, and was airborne for a distance of just over a quarter of a mile.

Cody regularly tethered his aircraft during engine test runs to a tree situated alongside the Balloon Factory and near to where he made the first take off. A metal replica of the tree now commemorates this historic first flight. [Figure 1]

Following Cody's flight other pioneers took to the air and military interest in powered aircraft slowly grew, the Balloon site becoming the home of His Majesty's Army Aircraft Factory, renamed the Royal Aircraft Factory in May 1912.

The 'Factory', as it became known locally, not only conducted flight research, but before and during the First World War designed and built aircraft for the Royal Flying Corps. Its SE 5a aircraft is considered by many to have been the outstanding fighter of the Allied air forces in that conflict, over 5,200 having been built by the Factory and under contract by Industry. [Figure 2]

One of the earliest Factory test pilots was Capt Geoffery de Havilland who left Farnborough in 1914 to found the famous de Havilland Aircraft Co. His flight test work was ably continued by Major Frank Goodden who tested many Factory designs until he was killed in a crash of an SE5 prototype [Figure 3]. Men like these started a tradition of research flying at Farnborough which continued for over 80 years.

Towards the end of 1916 under pressure from the rapidly expanding independent manufacturers, and a campaign by a few vociferous members of Parliament, the government decided that prototype and early production aircraft would no longer be constructed at the Factory, but that it would concentrate on government funded research into all aspects of aircraft design and flight. One result of this change was that pioneers, such as SE 5 aircraft designer H P Folland and Fred Green, who had developed the RAF series of aero engines, left Farnborough to set up their own aircraft firms or to lead design groups.

The Factory's change of function was confirmed in 1918 when it was renamed the Royal Aircraft Establishment (RAE), a name that was to become respected throughout the aviation world.

Figure 1. Metal replica of Cody's Tree with the 'Black Sheds' in the background. [DRA Crown Copyright]

Figure 2. Prototype SE 5 aircraft, November 1916. Major F W Goodden in the cockpit. [RAE Crown Copyright]

Figure 3. Major F W Goodden, Royal Aircraft Factory test pilot killed in a crash of an SE 5 aircraft on 28 January 1917. [RAE Crown Copyright]

ROYAL AIRCRAFT ESTABLISHMENT 1918-88

Although the number of RAE employees fell from about 5,000 to 1,400 in the inter-war years, with a corresponding reduction in research funding, the quality of the research work undertaken was high. It provided a foundation which was of great value during the anxious years of rearmament of the Royal Air Force before World War 2. Spurred by the threat of war, the number employed at RAE had risen to about 3,000 by 1938, of whom 550 were scientific and technical staff.

At the outbreak of war in September 1939, the airfield was still grass and biplanes could still be seen in front of the camouflaged hangars near the Farnborough Road. [Figure 4]

Work began on the airfield runways in 1940; this construction can be clearly seen in progress in a German aerial reconnaissance photograph of the airfield taken in September 1940. [Figure 5]

The RAE's technical departments and test facilities were kept extremely busy throughout the war years, work continuing at weekends and often through the night; the departments greatly increasing in number and size. There was a large increase in staff numbers: University professors, graduates, and skilled craftsmen, being directed to work in the Establishment under the War Emergency powers.

To accommodate the influx, houses throughout Farnborough were requisitioned for lodgings, some of the larger houses in Alexandra Road and neighbouring streets being so crammed full of RAE staff that they were likened to rabbit warrens. By early 1944 the total employed at the Establishment, including those dispersed to Outstations, had risen to a peak of about 9,000.

There was an inevitable retrenchment following the end of the war. In addition all of the flight test work of the Aerodynamics Department, and the Naval Aircraft Department, was transferred to Bedford in 1955. There it was to form part of what was to be the National Aeronautical Establishment, later to become RAE Bedford.

In the ensuing years a growing proportion of Farnborough's research effort went into providing the Aerospace industry and the Ministry of Defence project officers with basic information needed for guided weapon and missile design and specification. This aspect of RAE's activities was recognised in 1988 by a change of name to Royal Aerospace Establishment. It was followed in 1991 by the controversial reorganisation into the Defence Research Agency (DRA), which introduced competitive funding of the Establishment's research work for the first time.

Under the centralised DRA organisation, the functional naming of the Research Establishments was abolished; the Royal Aerospace Establishment losing its proud title to become the Defence Research Agency, Farnborough. This was followed by a declaration by the DRA that the airfield was "surplus to requirements", and as a result all Farnborough research flying transferred to the Ministry of Defence airfield at Boscombe Down, Wiltshire, in March 1994.

Throughout all of the ups and downs at Farnborough over the years, there fortunately remained on staff as a result of the long term policies of Senior 'Ministry' men and strong-minded Directors of the Establishment, a core of aircraft enthusiasts, scientists and pilots who took to the air regularly to further knowledge of aircraft flight and design. Those at the 'sharp end' in the air were supported by the painstaking research and development work carried out in the Establishment's technical offices, drawing offices, laboratories and workshops.

If one were to attempt to describe the achievements and highlights of the many years of research flying at RAE, it would be a major undertaking which would fill many volumes. For example, during just one of the war years, 11,640 successful research flights were made from Farnborough airfield on a wide range of tasks. However, it would be wrong to allow research flying at Farnborough to end without an attempt to illustrate the work in the air and the demands it made on the aircrew.

In the parachute packing bay of the Aircrew Survival Equipment Section at Farnborough, a wallboard list was started in 1925, the year when emergency escape parachutes were first introduced into the RAF. The purpose of the wallboard was to record those Establishment pilots, aircrew and civilian scientists flying as test observers, who saved their lives by parachute following an emergency in flight.

By 1991 there were 30 names and 23 aircraft on the list, providing both a random series of 'snapshots' of the range of research and experimental flying carried out over the years and a testimony to the determination and courage of RAE aircrew. [Figure 6]

The flights and parachute escapes listed are the subject of this book, but in describing them in detail the opportunity has also been taken to describe some of the background work in the RAE technical departments associated with that in the air. (The author makes no apologies for these diversions from the main theme, in common with many ex-RAE staff he feels that justice still remains to be done in recording the research work of the RAE.)

All of the aviators listed on the RAE wallboard were entitled to become members of the renowned Caterpillar Club, founded by parachute manufacturer Leslie Irvin in 1922. His Company donates a gold silkworm lapel pin to every person whose life has been saved by a parachute of basic Irvin design. To date there are some 32,000 members of the UK branch of the club, most of whom made emergency escapes by parachute during the Second World War. [Figure 7]

Figure 4. RAE and grass airfield in 1939. [RAE Crown Copyright]

GB 1077 b1

Nur für den Dienstgebrauch

Bild Nr. F 01036/40/065

Aufnahme vom 28.9.40.

Farnborough

Flugplatz

Länge (westl. Greenw.): 0° 46'

Nördl. Breite: 51° 17'

Zielhöhe über NN 69 m

Maßstab etwa: 1:19 500

500 0 500 1000 m

Lfl. Kdo. 3 Juli 1941

Karte 1:100 000

GB/E Bl. 34 c

Figure 5. German aerial reconnaissance photograph of the RAE and Aldershot (28 September 1940). The 'Factory' site (at top centre of photograph) is partially obscured by cloud, but runways under construction are clearly visible. [RAE Crown Copyright]

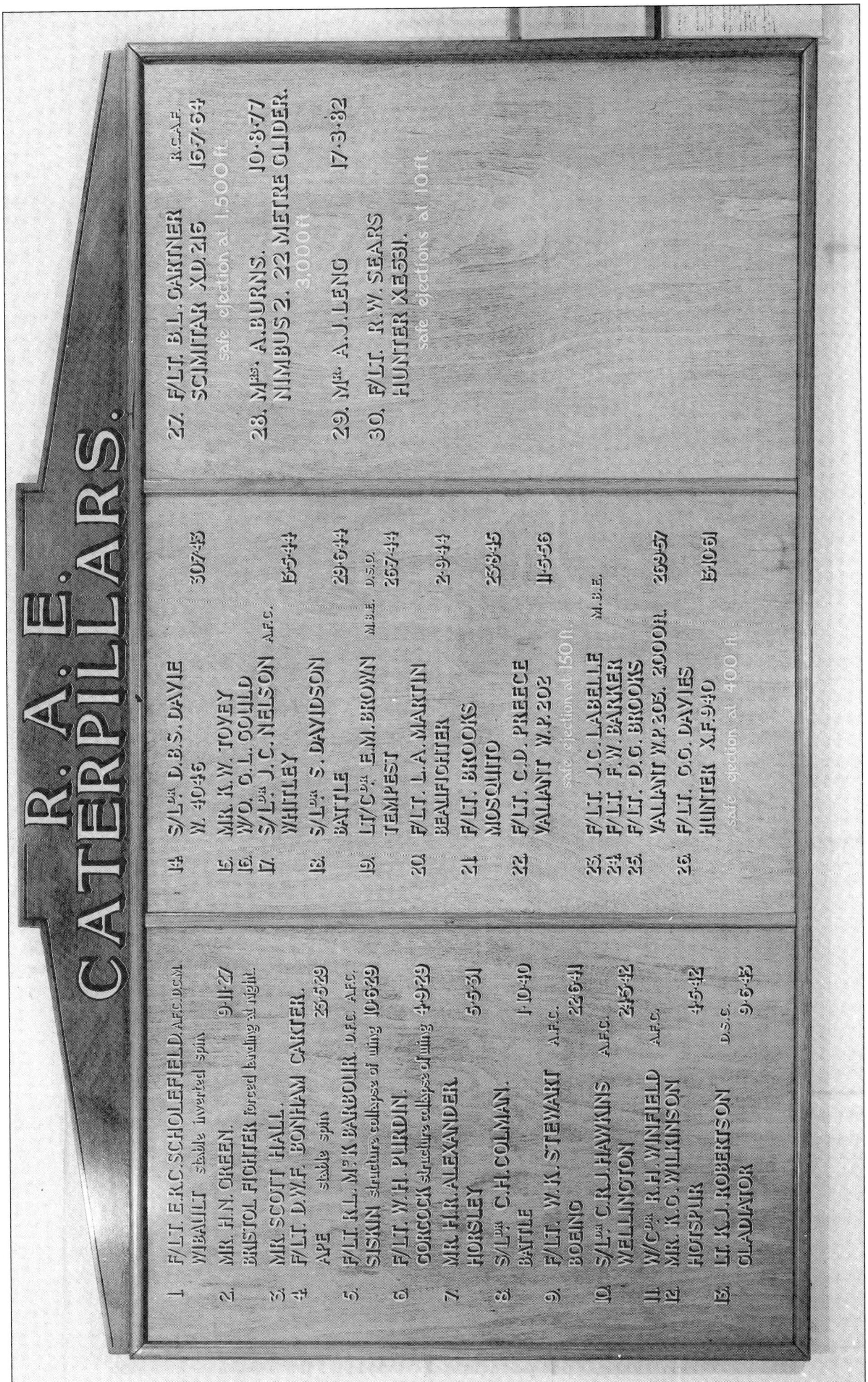

R. A. E.
CATERPILLARS.

1. F/LT. E.R.C. SCHOLEFIELD A.F.C. D.C.M.
WIBAULT stable inverted spin 9·11·27
2. MR. H.N. GREEN.
BRISTOL FIGHTER forced landing at night.
3. MR. SCOTT HALL.
4. F/LT. D.W.F. BONHAM CARTER.
APE stable spin 23·5·29
5. F/LT. R.L. McK BARBOUR. D.F.C. A.F.C.
SISKIN structure collapse of wing 10·6·29
6. F/LT. W.H. PURDIN.
GORCOCK structure collapse of wing 4·9·29
7. MR. H.R. ALEXANDER.
HORSLEY 5·5·31
8. S/LDR. C.H. COLMAN.
BATTLE 1·10·40
9. F/LT. W.K. STEWART A.F.C.
BOEING 22·6·41
10. S/LDR. C.R.J. HAWKINS A.F.C.
WELLINGTON 24·3·42
11. W/CDR. R.H. WINFIELD A.F.C.
12. MR. K.G. WILKINSON
HOTSPUR 4·5·42
13. LT. K.J. ROBERTSON D.S.C.
GLADIATOR 9·6·43
14. S/LDR. D.B.S. DAVIE
W. 4046 30·7·43
15. MR. K.W. TOVEY
16. W/O. G.L. GOULD
17. S/LDR. J.C. NELSON A.F.C.
WHITLEY 15·5·44
18. S/LDR. S. DAVIDSON
BATTLE 29·6·44
19. LT/CDR. E.M. BROWN M.B.E. D.S.O.
TEMPEST 26·7·44
20. F/LT. L.A. MARTIN
BEAUFIGHTER 2·9·44
21. F/LT. BROOKS
MOSQUITO 23·8·45
22. F/LT. C.D. PREECE
VALIANT W.P. 202 11·5·56
safe ejection at 150 ft.
23. F/LT. J.C. LABELLE M.B.E.
24. F/LT. F.W. BARKER
25. F/LT. D.G. BROOKS
VALIANT W.P. 203. 2000 ft. 26·9·57
26. F/LT. G.G. DAVIES
HUNTER X.F. 940 13·10·61
safe ejection at 400 ft.
27. F/LT. B.L. GARTNER R.C.A.F.
SCIMITAR X.D. 216 16·7·64
safe ejection at 1,500 ft.
28. MRS. A. BURNS. 10·8·77
NIMBUS 2. 22 METRE GLIDER.
3,000 ft.
29. MR. A.J. LENG 17·3·82
30. F/LT. R.W. SEARS
HUNTER XE 531.
safe ejections at 10 ft.

Figure 6. RAE Caterpillars recorded on a wallboard in the RAE parachute packing room. [RAE Crown Copyright]

Figure 7. Leslie Irvin in 1933, wearing the standard RAF seat parachute of the period. [via Aeroplane Monthly]

RAE CATERPILLARS — EARLY DAYS

The first name on the RAE list is Flt Lt E R C Scholefield, who was wearing a parachute for the very first time when he took off on 1 July 1926 to test a new Vickers Wibault Scout all metal-monoplane. During testing the aircraft went into a violent inverted spin, and although Scholefield tried all the known procedures he was unable to recover the aircraft into normal flight.

While the aircraft was still spinning upside down, he released his seat straps and fell from the cockpit, operating his parachute when well clear of the aircraft to become the second member of the UK branch of the Caterpillar Club. The aircraft was still inverted when it struck the ground. [Figures 8 and 9]

There is something of a mystery about this first board entry, as in 1926 Scholefield was a Vickers test pilot and the flight was being made from Brooklands. The reasons for this discrepancy are lost in the past, but Scholefield had been an RAE test pilot before he joined Vickers and it is possible that his parachute was packed at Farnborough.

Sadly he was not wearing a parachute on the day two years later when the aeroplane he was testing disintegrated in flight. Group Captain Peter Hearn in 'The Sky People' recalls the American maxim: 'He never needed one again'.

On 9 November 1927 Fg Off Mackenzie Richards and Mr H Green took off from Farnborough airfield in a Bristol Fighter to investigate the performance of experimental night flying aids. The aircraft went out of control in the darkness over East Grinstead, Sussex while on its way to Croydon airport for landing experiments. Mr Green was ordered to jump at 2,000ft altitude, and made the first successful escape by parachute at night. Unfortunately by the time the pilot gave up his attempt to regain control and abandoned the aircraft it was too low for his parachute to inflate fully and he was killed.

On 23 May 1929 Flt Lt D W F Bonham Carter and Mr Stuart Scott-Hall had to make an emergency parachute escape from an Armstrong Whitworth Ape 'variable configuration experimental biplane', which stalled and then spun into the ground at Cove, Farnborough. It was a fortunate escape for both pilot and scientist, as they later went on to have distinguished careers in British aviation. [Figure 10]

The special research aircraft was probably a good idea, enabling the effect of major changes in configuration to be investigated in a series of flights. But RAE legend has it that it was also the cause of the aircraft's downfall, as 'tailplane up' incidence wound on during stalling tests, could not be reversed rapidly enough to aid recovery from an unexpected spin.

The spin, however, was no longer the intractable problem it had appeared to be to the early aviators, largely as a result of courageous research flights during the First World War by Professor F A Lindemann (later Lord Cherwell) and Major F W Goodden, to investigate methods of recovery from deliberately entered spins of 'Factory' designed BE 2 and FE 8 aircraft.

In the early 1920s though, aircraft of new design appeared which if stalled went into a flat spin and could not be recovered by control movements previously found effective. Work at RAE to understand this problem was successfully completed by a detailed theoretical study of the balance of forces and moments in the spin and of methods of recovery from the motion, presented in an RAE report of 1926, 'The Spinning Of Aeroplanes', by S B Gates and L W Bryant. Sydney Barrington Gates, is however, best known for his many years of work in producing, with Hilda Lyon, a series of 'classic' RAE Aerodynamics Department reports which formulated the theoretical basis of aircraft longitudinal static and manoeuvring stability, together with methods of interpretation of flight test results. Their clearly written reports were widely used throughout the UK aircraft industry and the research and test Establishments.

During Gates' working life he wrote over 130 technical reports and memoranda, either singly or in association with other RAE aerodynamicists, covering completely new ground on aerodynamics and flight testing. After the United States entered World War 2 he travelled to USA, early in 1942, with Morien Morgan (later Sir Morien Morgan), to hand over a whole sack load of RAE reports on the handling characteristics of UK bomber and fighter aircraft, and to discuss common problems with aeronautical research workers in the States. Morgan wrote in an appreciation of Gates, following his death in 1973, that he had an even greater reputation internationally than at home. His theoretical work and keen physical penetration of a problem was recognised in 1950, when he was elected a Fellow of the Royal Society, and later by his rank of Chief Scientific Officer, one of the few RAE scientists to attain this grade on individual merit.

The year 1929 seems to have been a bad one for wing structures. The RAE Caterpillar's board records that Flt Lt R L Mc K Barbour in an Armstrong Whitworth Siskin on 10 June and Flt Lt Purdin in a Gloster Gorcock on 4 September both had to bale out when their aircraft suffered wing flutter and failure in test flights. [Figure 11]

One suspects that, as usual at RAE, these failures concentrated minds wonderfully well and led to considerable activity in the then Airworthiness Department in developing special test rigs. Particularly notable were the massive 'Temple' and 'Cathedral' structural test rigs in which simulated aerodynamic loadings could be applied to aircraft structures by numerous screw jacks and lever systems. These rigs later played a valuable part in World War 2 in strength testing and improving the structural efficiency of a whole series of fuselages and wings, including the wings of Avro's Lancaster and Lincoln bombers and de Havilland's versatile Mosquito aircraft. [Figure 13] (Following modifications to the Mosquito wing, the final test achieved a valuable 40% higher breaking load than the first design).

There is a hidden story behind the laconic entry on the Caterpillar board for Mr R H Alexander, who escaped in 1931 from an all-metal Hawker Horsley, an aircraft type used by the RAE as an instrumented flying test bed for early versions of the Rolls Royce Buzzard engine and the Merlin, an engine destined to become famous during World War 2. While manoeuvring a few hundred feet above RAE, the Buzzard-engined aircraft suffered a jammed aileron control and the pilot Flt Lt H R D Waghorn and test observer Alexander took to their parachutes. Both landed on a roof of buildings at RAE, but whilst Alexander escaped with slight injuries, Waghorn, who was something of a national hero after winning the 1929 Schneider Trophy contest for Britain in a Supermarine S6, fell from the roof of a tall building on to a lamp post, sustaining injuries from which he died two days later. [Figure 12]

Figure 8. A French-built Wibault 7.C.1 from which the Vickers Wibault Scout evolved. [via Philip Jarrett]

Figure 9. Flt Lt E R C Scholefield standing smiling beside his crashed Vichers Wibault Scout. [via Group Capt P Hearn]

Figure 10. The second Armstrong Whitworth Ape J-7754, from which Messrs Bonham Carter and Scott Hall departed in a great hurry on 23 May 1929. Note the extent to which the cockpit-controlled tailplane incidence could be adjusted in flight. [via Philip Jarrett]

Figure 11. J-7502, one of the three Gloster Gorcocks built. Flt Lt Purdin baled out of J-7501 after it broke up over Aldershot, Hampshire on 4 September 1929. [via Aeroplane Monthly]

Figure 12. Hawker Horsley J-8932, powered by an experimental Rolls Royce Buzzard engine, from which R H Alexander took to the silk on 4 May 1931. [via Philip Jarrett]

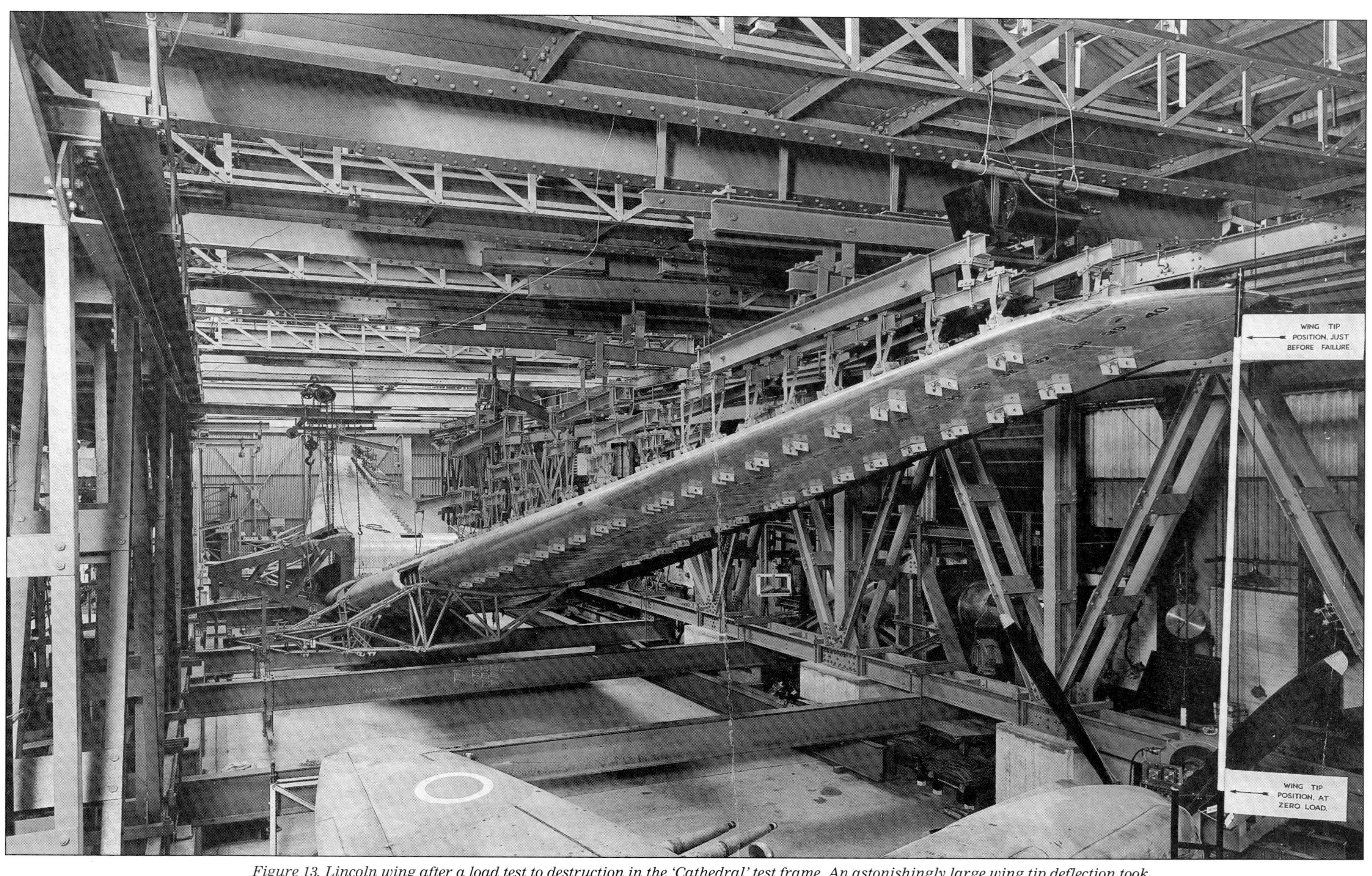

Figure 13. Lincoln wing after a load test to destruction in the 'Cathedral' test frame. An astonishingly large wing tip deflection took place before the wing broke. [RAE Crown Copyright]

WORLD WAR 2 ESCAPES

The board entries following the Horsley incident and covering the World War 2 period are understandably brief, as are many of the wartime RAE flight logs. But by combining information available from flight logs, official records now made public, and in some cases personal accounts related to the author, the stories behind the wartime escapes have been established.

Sqn Ldr C H Coleman's bale out from a Fairey Battle bomber on 1 October 1940, took place during a flight from Exeter airfield, the Air Defence Investigation Department of RAE having moved to Exeter just before the outbreak of war. The Air Defence Group investigated many novel ideas, mainly for the defence of airfields, ranging from special barrage balloon systems, to rocket-launched parachute and cable systems and aerial mines.

Sqn Ldr Colman was returning to Exeter after conducting tests with dummy aerial mines descending over a trials range situated on the coast near Bridgwater, Somerset, when an anti-spin parachute was inadvertently streamed from his Battle aircraft in flight. This entangled with the tail controls and caused the aircraft to become uncontrollable. Although Colman successfully escaped by parachute, his flight test observer, Mr Oliver Tipple, was killed when the aircraft crashed near the range.

It is believed that Lord Cherwell, then Scientific Adviser to the Cabinet, was behind the rather unsuccessful aerial mine project; but place a well-chosen group of scientists together, and give them time and space to think and experiment, and the 'spin off' can be very worthwhile. [Figure 14]

The Exeter scientists started work on the very first radio and photo-electric operated proximity fuses for shells and warheads, and on scatter bombs and probability theory. The group also flight tested the very successful gyro gunsight, designed and developed by Armament Department, RAE, which automatically determined the amount of offset required in deflection shooting. The gunsight was introduced into RAF fighter and bomber aircraft early in 1944 and immediately greatly improved the success rate in combat. It was manufactured in quantity by the Ferranti Company; almost all RAF operational fighter aircraft being fitted with the sight by the time of the invasion of Europe. [Figure 15]

On 22 June 1941, Fg Off Dr William Stewart, AFC of the RAF Physiological Laboratory, forerunner of the RAF Institute of Aviation Medicine, was flown to West Raynham airfield in a Boston aircraft, piloted by Flt Lt Humpherson, DFC. The object of his visit was to investigate possible causes of the loss of six out of twenty early Boeing B17C 'Flying Fortress' aircraft, supplied to 90 Squadron RAF by the Americans for operational evaluation. Dr Stewart was to fly in Fortress AN 522, accompanied by Flt Lt Humpherson, to investigate possible pilot and aircrew errors and in particular the performance of the aircrew oxygen system installed in the aircraft. [Figure 16]

After about 50 minutes steady climbing flight, the aircraft flew into a violent thunderstorm at an altitude of 31,000ft and met severe air turbulence and icing conditions during which the aircraft went out of control and entered a spiral dive.

Against heavy 'g' loads, Dr Stewart coolly fought his way along the fuselage into the rear section to await the inevitable break-up of the aircraft. The tail section eventually broke off and Dr Stewart was then able to extricate himself and stream his parachute at a low altitude. He was the only survivor of the eight members of the crew and was able to make a valuable report on the problems encountered on the fateful flight. A dorsal fin was added as a modification to later marks of the Fortress.

Early in 1942 following night bombing attacks on Exeter airfield, which damaged the RAE hangars, the Research Flight of the Air Defence Department moved to Churchstanton airfield near Taunton. The airfield, now disused, is situated high up in the Blackdown hills in an area of 'outstanding natural beauty'. Mr A J 'Digger' Armstrong, who was Flight foreman at Exeter and Churchstanton, and later became a much respected RAE apprentice supervisor, spoke to the author in 1994 about the work at Churchstanton, 'Digger' was then 95 years old, but could remember every detail of his RAE career as if it was yesterday. (Sadly he died in February 1996 during the preparation of this book). 'Digger' well remembered the beauty of the countryside around Churchstanton, but also spoke with some feeling about the isolated situation of the airfield and the freezing cold winds which blew across it in the Winter of 1941/2.

As part of its work, the Flight was engaged in deliberately flying into barrage-balloon cables to investigate the performance of Martin-Baker cable cutting devices attached to the wing leading edges of RAF bombers.

On 24 March 1942, Vickers Wellington P 9210 fitted with a wing-mounted cable cutter, was deliberately flown into a barrage balloon cable by Sqn Ldr C R 'Tiger' Hawkins. The work was so dangerous that only Hawkins was aboard the aircraft. He hit the cable with the port wing, but the cable passed intact over the cutter and then into the port engine and rotating propeller skewing the Wellington around and on to its back, breaking off the tail section from the fuselage. Fortunately Hawkins managed to force his way through a small cockpit side window, smashing his goggles in the process, to make a successful parachute descent. The Wellington, minus tail, crashed one mile West of Pawlett Church, near Bridgwater, Somerset. [Figure 17]

From 1940 on the RAE was involved in the build up, virtually from scratch, of the British Airborne Forces. Static-line operated troop parchutes were developed, gliders designed and tested and glider towing techniques evolved in a very short space of time. Typical of the spirit of those days, was the co-operation between Irvin GB Ltd and GQ Parachute Co: who together developed the X type parachute assembly, used by British paratroopers throughout the war.

Much of the flight test work on Hotspur, Horsa, and Hamilcar gliders, was carried out by the RAE Aero Airborne Section using runways constructed early in 1942, at the nearby Hartford Bridge airfield (later re-named Blackbushe). The Section was at the airfield until mid 1943, returning to Farnborough when Hartford became an operational base for Douglas Boston and North American Mitchell squadrons.

On 4 May 1942, as part of the glider flight research, Ken Wilkinson of Aero Airborne was on tow in a General Aircraft Hotspur troop-carrying glider to demonstrate an automatic towing system, aimed at enabling towed flight at night. Two VIPs were also on board, together with Wg Cdr Dr Roland Winfield of the Physiological Laboratory.

The Whitley tug and the glider were flown into cloud, where the tug pilot unfortunately throttled back and began a descent; the glider then started to overtake its tug and a large loop developed in the tow rope. As the Whitley pilot applied power again, the tow rope tightened across the top of the glider, removing the whole of the cockpit canopy and part of the nose. In the process it struck the pilot Flt Lt D B Davie on the head and left him bleeding and flying only by instinct.

The Whitley pilot realising the glider was in trouble then released the tow rope, but Davie was initially unable to release his end of the rope and, forced into a nose dive, shouted to the test observers to "jump". What happend next has become one of many RAE legends, fortunately one with a happy ending.

Wilkinson made a deliberate decision to leave the now open cockpit, away from the trailing rope, but the other observers left from the opposite side, where one had the misfortune to become entangled in the rope, damaging his parachute and resulting in a high rate of descent and injury on landing. Wilkinson landed upside down in a tree in a wood near Caesar's Camp, Aldershot, and was careful to climb on to a strong branch before releasing his harness. He walked away without a scratch to continue a career which included becoming the Chairman of British European Airways and then being asked to tackle the problems of Rolls Royce, following its enforced bankruptcy in 1972. Having successfully put Rolls Royce back on its feet, he joined British Airways and retired as Vice Chairman.

Wg Cmdr Winfield, who had previous parachuting experience, made a landing near a public house at Farnham, Surrey, and legend has it that he calmly strolled into the bar with his parachute rolled up under his arm, to chat with the landlord and drink a beer, before telephoning the RAE to be collected.

Davie remained in the glider and fortunately made a partial recovery from the blow he had received to release the flailing tow rope and make a heavy landing on the edge of the RAE airfield.

On those occasions when Wilkinson could be persuaded to tell the story of his escape, he would also recount the tale of his special spectacles, lost during his parachute descent. These were almost impossible to obtain in wartime and he put in a request to the Ministry for their replacement. The claim was disallowed by an Administrator who wrote a formal and unsympathetic letter in return, containing a gem of officialese, "I have been directed by my superiors to enquire why before abandoning your aircraft you did not first replace your spectacles in the receptacle provided and then into your pocket."

One can only remark that the official, and his superiors, must have been short of imagination; with the pilot dazed and bleeding and half of the glider nose and canopy torn off, no doubt the last thing on Wilkinson's mind was the care of his spectacles. Wilkinson had the letter specially framed, and it eventually ended up on the wall of the then Deputy Director, William Perring's office, as a classic example of the official mind.

For Wg Cmdr Dr Roland Winfield, AFC, the other Hotspur 'Caterpillar', this was just another incident in an eventful career at RAE. By the end of the war, he had flown on 120 operational missions to study the effect of fatigue and fear on aircrew performance, and had written a number of valuable reports on his findings. Winfield must have led a charmed life for statistically his chances of survival from 120 operations were minimal.

Not much is known about the cause of the loss of Gladiator K7946 on 9 June 1943. Flight logs indicate the aircraft was carrying an aerodynamic test vehicle when the aircraft suddenly rolled into an inverted position from which recovery could not be effected by the pilot, Lt K Robertson, DSC. Robertson baled out at 2,000ft altitude, the aircraft crashing in the grounds of Minley Manor near Farnborough (then the Headquarters of the Intelligence Corps).

The Gladiator is believed to have been regularly used for Meteorological Flight purposes and is known to have taken off to patrol Farnborough airfield, accompanied by a Spitfire and a Hurricane, whenever the air raid sirens sounded during the latter half of 1940. The armed patrol was organised as a result of the daylight bombing attack on the RAE of 16 August 1940 by eight Ju 88 bombers. Only about half of the bombs dropped fell on RAE in a line running from the Director's office to the engine test beds and Mess tennis courts. The RAE Transport Section building was badly damaged and three RAE members of the Local Defence Volunteers (later Home Guard), who had taken up their posts in a blockhouse nearby, were killed by a direct hit. [Figure 18]

When an imminent raid warning arrived, there was often a desperate race amongst pilots not to be left with the elderly Gladiator. Amusing stories circulated during 1940 of pilots pedalling furiously on standard RAF issue bicycles to be first at the aircraft dispersal, with many 'dirty tricks', such as mysterious flat tyres and 'accidental collisions' between riders taking place.

Early in 1943 the first jet propelled aircraft to fly at RAE whistled across the airfield, making a great impression on everyone at the Establishment. The aircraft was the second of the two Gloster E28/39 research aircraft built, W 4046/G. (The G denoted that a permanent RAF security guard was required on the aircraft). The aircraft was powered by Frank Whittle's turbo jet engine (a Rover-built W2B in this case).

Sqn Ldr D Davie, now promoted from Flight Lieutenant, flew this historic research aircraft intensively during May-July 1943 to determine accurately for the first time the performance of a jet engine and aircraft at altitude. On 30 July 1943, Davie was flying W 4046/G at 37,000ft when the ailerons became immovable, resulting in a complete loss of flying control and the aircraft entering an inverted spiral, forcing Davie to leave the aircraft at altitude. (The subsequent accident investigation, by the RAE's Fred Jones, showed the airleron seizure to be due to the effects of the very low temperature at altitude on the dissimilar metals of the control runs and the wing structure).

Davie baled out over Guildford at an altitude of 33,000ft and made the longest free-fall on record at that time before pulling his parachute ripcord. His oxygen mask had been torn from his face by the air forces on leaving the cockpit, but while free-falling he had the presence of mind to put the broken emergency oxygen tube in his mouth; thus he retained consciousness until a lower altitude was reached where he could safely operate his parachute. However, this was not the end of his troubles for during tumbling free-fall his flying boots came off and his feet were badly affected by frost-bite. [Figure 19]

The turbo-jet propulsion engine installed in the E28/39 aircraft, flown by Davie, was the result of the pioneering work of Sir Frank Whittle, who started to design a centrifugal flow turbo-jet engine in 1929, when a Pilot Officer in the RAF. It is now history that as a result of Whittle's determination and engineering ability, his was the first British jet engine to fly, in the first of two Gloster E28/39 research aircraft, W 4041/G, in May 1941.

Research work leading to a gas turbine engine was in fact first proposed by the RAE in 1926, three years before the then Plt Off Whittle started his life's work. Dr A A Griffiths wrote a classic RAE report 'An aerodynamic theory of turbine design' that showed a very efficient axial flow compressor and turbine could be designed by the new theory, detailed the advantages to be gained by the gas turbine engine, and proposed that research work leading to a gas turbine, driving a propeller, should be started.

Unfortunately apart from useful compressor and turbine blade experiments at RAE in 1929, it was 1937 before external funding for gas turbine work was given the full support of the Aeronautical Research Committee. The Air Ministry then authorised RAE and Metropolitan Vickers to start major experimental work and design a turbo-jet engine for aircraft.

During 1938 and 1939, the RAE completed research work on the multi-stage axial flow compressor, and in 1940 and 1941, collaborated with the firm of Metropolitan Vickers on the design of the F2 turbo jet engine. The finalised engine featured a 9 stage axial flow compressor and a 2 stage turbine designed by Dr Griffith's methods. This arrangement was chosen, in preference to a centrifugal flow design, on the grounds that the improved efficiency and reduction of frontal area, more than compensated for the greater mechanical complexity. By 1942 several engines had been manufactured and on bench test delivered the then high static thrust of over 2,000lb.

The design of aircraft to be powered by the radically new jet engines was investigated by the Gloster Aircraft Company and RAE during 1939. Wind tunnel tests on scale models of the Gloster E28/39 aircraft and the F9/40, the first jet propelled aircraft intended for RAF service, being completed in the RAE wind tunnels in 1940. A full scale Whittle/Rover W2B engine, mounted on an F9/40 wing, was also tested in the 24ft diameter wind tunnel in 1942, to investigate intake, nacelle and jet flow interactions. A vertical duct in the tunnel mouth was specially designed to take the jet efflux out of the tunnel airstream which was cooled by water sprays around the duct entry. [Figure 21]

Flight testing of the first British axial flow jet engine, the RAE/Metropolitan Vickers F2, started at RAE in June 1943 in a special installation in the tail of Avro Lancaster BT 308/G. The F2 design became the first axial flow jet engine to power an aircraft, the Gloster F9/40 DG 204/G. Flight tests started at RAE in November 1943, code named 'Rampage' and classified 'Most Secret'. [Figure 22]

On 4 January 1944, the indomitable Sqn Ldr Davie, AFC, now CO of Turbine Flight, RAE, took off in DG 204/G powered by two F2 engines, on an altitude performance climb to 30,000ft to investigate engine surging characteristics. The day was cold, with a clear blue sky, and many of the RAE's staff returning from their lunch break stopped to watch the aircraft glinting in the sun trailing its jet plumes at an altitude of about 20,000ft.

Those in the know, which included many of the RAE's apprentices, were aware that Davie was flight testing the axial flow jet engine on which Engines Department had carried out so much basic research work over the years. But to the watchers' dismay, the aircraft suddenly performed large gyrations in flight and pieces of the aircraft began to fall in the direction of the airfield.

Scientist/test observer Brian Attwell, returning to the airfield in a Vickers Wellington, after completing tests on a new aerial reconnaissance camera, remembers to this day his emotions as he, and his pilot Frank Nettleton, watched the tragedy from the air. An RAF engineer officer walking down the hill from the Officers' Mess towards the famous Farnborough 'Black Sheds' had the unfortunate experience of seeing Davie's body, with parachute unoperated, crash through the roof of a store behind the sheds, while by an extraordinary chance the detached tail of the aircraft landed on the roof of the RAE foundry, close to the engine test beds. In losing Douglas Davie, the RAE had lost a much respected airman, an energetic and popular test pilot, whose loss was keenly felt by all who knew him at RAE. [Figure 20]

Later investigation of the wreckage of the engine and aircraft showed that a crystalline fracture of the material of the compressor drum of the port engine had led to the disintegration of the engine, which sliced its way through the aircraft. Davie had tried to escape, but after fighting his way out of the cockpit, at between 15,000ft and 20,000ft altitude, he was swept rearwards by the air forces on to the aircraft's tailplane and mortally injured. [Figure 23]

Although the loss of Davie and his aircraft was a setback to the RAE programme of jet work, F2 engine development work continued and flight testing of the engine completed. It is relevant to note that only a few years later many of the high thrust jet engines under development by the industry were of the axial flow type initiated by the RAE. By 1948 the Armstrong Siddely F9/ Sapphire engine, a direct descendant of the F2, was delivering a static thrust of 7,000lbs. Later versions of the engine powered the English Electric P1a, the first British aircraft to exceed the speed of sound in level flight, in 1954.

During 1944/45 Turbine Flight RAE also flight tested Gloster F9/40, DG 206/G, fitted with de Havilland H1 jet engines. These centrifugal flow jet engines, were based on Whittle's concept and were centrally mounted on the wings. [Figure 24]

The tragic loss of Sqn Ldr Davie underlined the need for an assisted escape system for aircrew, and added urgency to work in progress to establish the overall acceleration and final escape velocity needed to achieve a safe ejection from an aircraft; also to discover how the human body reacted to violent accelerations. Much of the medical data was obtained by the experiments of Sqn Ldr Dr W Stewart, who lying on his back in a seat fixed to a rocket-propelled trolley, was fired along rails to be arrested rapidly by hydraulic rams and subjected to peak values of up to 12 'g'*. The mathematics of the ejection were established by Prof A D Young of Aerodynamics Department. This work took place in collaboration with the Martin Baker Aircraft Co, who have continued to design and manufacture advanced ejection seats which are supplied to Air Forces all over the world.

In May 1944 the three-man crew of a Whitley fitted with experimental spring tabs on its elevator, were engaged in flight tests to measure elevator 'stick' forces per 'g' in 'pull outs' following a dive. No trouble was experienced until, in a dive at 180 knots and 2,600 engine rpm, the starboard engine began to overspeed and shortly afterwards flames and glycol fluid were seen coming out of the engine.

The pilot of the Whitley was Sqn Ldr J G 'Jimmy' Nelson, an ex-Eagle Squadron American, whose report on the incident was brief and to the point: "After taking all the proper remedial actions there was no improvement and I ordered Mr Tovey and W O Gould to bale out, and they went overboard with the greatest ease and discipline. I stayed with the aircraft about four minutes longer in a final endeavour to put out the fire, but when I saw the engine cowling burn away I left also. After I left the aircraft the wing fell off at the starboard engine. On landing I was picked up by the Medical Officer from Aldermaston and after making a statement to the Station Intelligence Officer I returned to base."

On 29 June 1944, Sqdn Ldr S Davidson was carrying out tests in a Fairey Battle to determine the effects on a pilot of 'black out'** during high 'g' banked turns. Under the loading resulting from a very high 'g' turn, part of the aircraft structure failed and the bomber went out of control, forcing Davidson to take to his parachute.

Entry No 19 on the board in the RAE's Aircrew Survival Equipment Section, lists an escape by an outstanding RAE test pilot, Lt Cdr Eric 'Winkle' Brown. Brown was with the Aerodynamics Flight from 1944 to 1949 when the Flight's pilots were making courageous efforts to explore the unknown field of high speed flight close to the speed of sound.

On 26 July 1944, Brown was flying Hawker

---

* Under an acceleration of 12 'g' a body experiences a load 12 times its normal weight (1 'g').

** Under heavy 'g' loads, the blood supply to the brain is reduced and can lead to temporary unconsciousness and blindness.

Tempest V, JN 735, which had been fitted with an engine modified to give abnormally high power for short periods, using a special 150 octane fuel. The modification was intended to give the aircraft additional speed to catch and shoot down the fast-flying V1 flying bomb.

During a low level performance run to determine the maximum speed obtainable, the engine started to misfire badly until there was a lound bang and the windscreen was covered by a spray of oil. Intense white flames then came through the cockpit floor, and when Brown had to take his feet off the rudder pedals because of the fierce heat, he decided that it was time to leave the aircraft. On trying to escape he found himself jammed against the open hood by the air pressure, until, at about 1,200ft above the ground, he managed to reach into the cockpit and bank the aircraft sharply so that he was thrown out, streaming his parachute almost simultaneously. He landed in a shallow pond in the ground of Headley Park, near Bordon, Hants, some 200 yards from where the Tempest hit the ground and exploded.

Captain Eric Brown relates in his book 'Testing for Combat', how he was then confronted by a large and irate black bull waiting for him to leave the pond — very obviously annoyed at the disturbance to the peace of his field. It was some time before the local police, fire brigade and the bull's owner could extricate Captain Brown from his new predicament.

The high-speed flight test work previously mentioned, which took place during 1943-45, was remarkable. A number of piston-engined aircraft were put into high speed dives by Aero Flight pilots to establish their limiting Mach Number* and high speed flight characteristics. Among the aircraft tested in this way was the Mustang, Thunderbolt, Tempest, and Spitfire Mk XI and 21. Particular use was made of the Spitfire to make a full scale test comparison with results obtained using scale models of the aircraft in the RAE high speed tunnel; the tests providing a check on the accuracy of the wind tunnel results.

The pressurised high speed wind tunnel was completed in 1942, to become the most advanced facility in the UK at that time. It provided a vital research facility which allowed aircraft models of up to 6ft wing span to be tested at airspeeds of up to 600 mph. The pressurised tunnel was constructed in steel plate, the airflow being circulated by a 16ft diameter fan driven by a 4,000 hp motor. Design and construction posed many problems, which were solved by the outstanding team of RAE aerodynamicists led by William Perring and professional engineers headed by the Sir William Arrol Company. [Figure 25]

From 1942 onwards, long hours were worked to provide aerodynamic data on future designs. By the end of the war, tunnel tests had been made on the Spitfire, Hawker Typhoon and Tempest V, Gloster E28/39 and F9/40 (Meteor), Westland Welkin, Gloster E5/42 and Miles E23/43 (M52) research aircraft. In addition many basic research tests were made of wing shapes, sections, and control surfaces, to investigate their suitability for future high speed fighter and bomber aircraft. [Figure 26]

Post war the tunnel was extensively modified to provide a valuable transonic test facility. In 1956, the Fairey Delta 2 aircraft, which had been tunnel tested, broke the World Speed Record, reaching 1132 mph, and in later years tunnel testing of scale models of Harrier and Tornado aircraft contributed to their success. The high speed tunnel was finally decommissioned in 1993 after providing some 50 years of invaluable service to British Aviation.

Although the aircraft high speed dive tests taking place during the war years were simple in principle, they were dangerous for the pilots. At speeds approaching the speed of sound, aircraft experienced nose-down changes of trim as shock waves formed in the air flow over the wing, and large elevator angles were needed, with heavy pilot's stick** forces, to prevent the dive becoming irrecoverable.

In his book 'Wings on my sleeve' (Airlife 1978) 'Winkle' Brown relates that when diving a Spitfire at Mach 0.86 the aircraft started shaking badly and rocking from side to side. He had to pull the equivalent of 60 lb on the stick, his physical limit, to stop the dive steepening further, and the airspeed increasing to a critical value where loss of control made it impossible to effect a recovery from the dive.

But Sqdn Ldr A F Martindale, the CO of Aero Flight during 1944-46, reached Mach 0.91 (a true airspeed of 620 mph at 27,000ft) in an extraordinary dive from 40,000ft early in 1944. This was the highest fully-documented speed ever achieved by a piston-engined aircraft.

On 27 April he repeated this test in Spitfire EN 409, a pre-production Mk XI, but this time he heard a fearful explosion at 27,000ft altitude. The aircraft "shook from end to end" and Martindale partially 'blacked out' under positive 'g' loads. When he recovered his sight again, with the cockpit full of smoke, Martindale should perhaps have baled out and added his name to those on the RAE Caterpillar board, but he decided to stay with the aircraft.

As the windscreen cleared of oil he saw that the propeller was missing, but with great skill he was able to glide back and land on Farnborough airfield, thus saving the automatic observer records and the test instrumentation. The propeller and reduction gear had been completely lost due to overspeeding during the steep dive. An

---

* Mach Number is the ratio of the aircraft flight speed to the speed at which sound travels in air, at the test altitude (760 mph at ground level).

** The pilot's control column is referred to as the 'stick' by pilots and engineers.

estimate of the position of the Spitfire's centre of gravity, following the loss of these components, shows that it was an extraordinary feat for Martindale to have controlled the aircraft in the air, let alone land it back at Farnborough. [Figure 27]

The instrumentation was then transferred to Spitfire Mk XI PL 827 and the trials recommenced. During a further test dive, Martindale suffered a complete supercharger failure and engine fire. He was unable to see Farnborough because of cloud cover and, in attempting a forced-landing, swerved to avoid high tension wires and crashed in a copse on Whitmore Common, Surrey. Despite back injuries, he was able to remove the vital automatic observer records of the test from the burning aircraft. He was later awarded the Air Force Cross for his courageous work.

Further high speed test work was completed in 1945 using a Griffon engined Spitfire Mk 21 with a strengthened wing from which guns, blisters, and so on had been removed to reduce aerodynamic drag. [Figure 28]

Throughout the years of development of the various Marks of Spitfire, Supermarine and RAE worked well together. RAE made a number of contributions, ranging from the ducted radiator of 1935, which solved engine cooling problems, to wing flutter calculations and joint work on high speed handling and performance improvements. This co-operation was marked on 30 June 1950 by the presentation of a solid bronze model of a Spitfire to the RAE's Experimental Flying Department by Vickers Supermarine. It has been column-mounted and now has an honoured place in the RAF Officers' Mess garden. [Figure 29]

The series of high speed tests on a number of wartime fighters clearly established the relatively thin wing of the Spitfire as being superior in performance at very high speeds. The tests also demonstrated the need for future fighters to have effective power-assisted flight controls and high thrust jet engines, to counter the effect of shock wave drag, if transonic flight was to be achieved.

The results of these tests were distributed in the usual way as RAE reports and memoranda and many of the lessons learnt were incorporated in the Miles M52 research aircraft. This was being built during 1944-45 to be used by the Aerodynamics Flight Division to investigate flight at transonic and supersonic speeds.

The M52 was of advanced design, having a very thin wing with a root thickness chord ratio of 7.5 per cent and power operated flying controls, including an all moving tailplane. Propulsion was to be provided by a special W2/700 jet engine incorporating an afterburner and augmentor fan, being developed by the then Grp Capt Whittle.

Early in 1946, when the first aircraft was nearing completion, the project was cancelled at a high level in the Ministry of Aircraft Production. This was a considerable disappointment to many in the Flight Division, who, while accepting the aircraft was unlikely to have attained its specification speed of Mach 1.5 in level flight, were convinced that it would have achieved transonic flight under control following a dive from altitude (and proved the advanced flight control system).

In the event, the high speed research work continued with the swept wing de Havilland 108 jets, of which three were built. The first of these, TG 283, was a subsonic aircraft for the investigation of swept wing control problems, and the second TG 306, was a potentially supersonic version to assess the wing's high speed characteristics. It was in TG 306 that Geoffrey de Havilland, son of the firm's founder, lost his life in September 1946 when making a high speed test run, prior to an attempt on the world air speed record.

A modified version, VW 120, became available to the RAE early in 1949 and Lt Cmdr Brown reached Mach 0.985 in a dive from 45,000ft, but this was the limit that could be achieved in controlled flight.

In high speed flight at low altitudes another problem appeared, in the form of poorly damped longitudinal short period oscillations. On one flight below 10,000ft and at Mach 0.88, pitch oscillations could be induced by small control movements. This resulted in heavy fluctuating 'g' loads, rapidly increasing in magnitude, which could only be suppressed by a combination of careful piloting and good luck. Finally, restrictions were placed on the test programme, but sadly later in 1950, two very able pilots were killed, Sqdn Ldr J S R Muller Rowland, DSO, DFC in VW 120 on 15 February, 1950, and Sqdn Ldr G E C 'Jumbo' Genders, AFC, DFM who spun into the ground near Hartley Wintney, Hants during stalling trials of TG 283 on 1 May, 1950. [Figure 33]

As well as these two fatal accidents in the de Havilland 108s, Sqdn Ldr Whittome lost his life in a high speed dive in a Spitfire engaged in propeller research. Figure 30 shows these pilots and their colleagues in Aerodynamics Flight in May 1948.

On 2 September 1944, the Enemy Aircraft Flight at RAE, which flight tested and evaluated captured German aircraft throughout the war, received a request from an airfield near Toulouse in France to come and collect the first undamaged Heinkel He 177 bomber to be captured (by French Resistance members). Wg Cmdr R J 'Roly' Falk flew over in an RAE Hudson with an additional flight crew aboard, escorted by two Bristol Beaufighters, withdrawn from Wireless and Electrical Flight. ('Electrical' was in part a cover for airborne radar work.)

Arriving at the airfield after a long flight, as darkness fell, the Hudson landed safely, whereupon the runway lights were promptly extinguished, leaving the Beaufighters circling overhead. The two pilots, without radio communication with the airfield, decided to look for a more active airfield noted en route. Unfortunately the weather deteriorated and with his aircraft short of fuel, Sqdn Ldr 'Robin' Hood,

AFC, force-landed in Vichy France and Flt Lt 'Bob' Martin baled out near the French coast, becoming RAE Caterpillar No. 20.

Hood suffered injuries in landing and was taken to a field hospital where he was put into hospital pyjamas and told not to make himself too obvious because there were German wounded in the same ward. A day or two later, to Hood's surprise, a German officer appeared and started to distribute decorations to the wounded. Hood was even more surprised when the officer came over to his bed and in the chaotic conditions in the hospital, presented him with an Iron Cross (2nd class), apparently under the impression that he was a seriously wounded German. Sqdn Ldr Hood's Iron Cross was later loaned to the RAE Museum, where it became a prized exhibit.

The captured Heinkel He 177 A5, wearing RAF roundels and 'invasion stripes', was flown from France to Farnborough on 10 September 1944 for examination and flight test. It had been inscribed 'Prise de Guerre' on the side of the fuselage by its French Maquis captors. Of particular interest to the RAE was the unusual engine installation, each nacelle housing two engines coupled together to drive a four-bladed propeller. Also of interest was the radio altimeter and the spring tabs fitted to the control surfaces. [Figure 31]

Figure 14. A number of RAE scientists who later became famous names in the aviation world. In the front row centre is Dr H Roxbee Cox (Lord Kings Norton), on his right B Lockspieser (Sir Ben Lockspieser) and at the far left Major Marstrand, inventor of the non shimmy wheel and tyre. In the second row is Norman Cole, later Director General Guided Weapons and W Smith, later Head of Armaments Department, RAE. [DRA Crown Copyright]

Figure 15. RAE gyro gunsight under development in the laboratory. The semi-circular scale markings on the front of the sight give settings for the particular aircraft being engaged. The graticule sight is projected on to the sloping 'see through mirror' at the top of the sight. [DRA Crown Copyright]

Figure 16. Boeing 'Flying Fortress' AN 531 delivered to the RAF for evaluation in 1941. Fg Off Dr William Stewart was the sole survivor when Fortress Mk 1 AN 522 went out of control in a violent thunderstorm at 31,000 feet and broke up in the air on 22 June 1941. [via Aeroplane Monthly]

Figure 17. Sqdn Ldr C R Hawkins escaped by parachute on 24 March 1942 when Vickers Wellington P 9210 broke up in flight during barrage balloon cable cutting tests. Wellington Mk II P 9238 is illustrated. [via Aeroplane Monthly]

Figure 18. Aerial view of the main 'Factory' site showing bomb damage resulting from an attack by eight Ju 88 bombers on RAE — 16 August 1940. [RAE Crown Copyright]

Figure 19. The Gloster/Whittle jet research aircraft E28/39 W4041/G. Sqdn Ldr Davie baled out of W4046/G on 30 July 1943. [RAE Crown Copyright]

Figure 20. The late Sqdn Ldr Davie, AFC. The first airman to lose his life in a jet aircraft, on 4 January 1944. [DRA Crown Copyright]

Figure 21. A Whittle/Rover W2B jet engine installed in an F9/40 nacelle under test in the RAE 24ft wind tunnel in 1942. [DRA Crown Copyright]

Figure 22. The first British axial flow jet engine, the RAE/Metropolitan Vickers F2 engine. [RAE Crown Copyright]

Figure 23. Gloster F9/40, DG 204/G, with underwing-mounted RAE/Metropolitan Vickers F2 axial flow jet engines. Sqdn Ldr Davie lost his life in this aircraft when the port engine disintegrated in flight. [DRA Crown Copyright]

Figure 24. Gloster F9/40, DG 206/G, with de Havilland H1 jet engines centrally mounted on the wing. [DRA Crown Copyright]

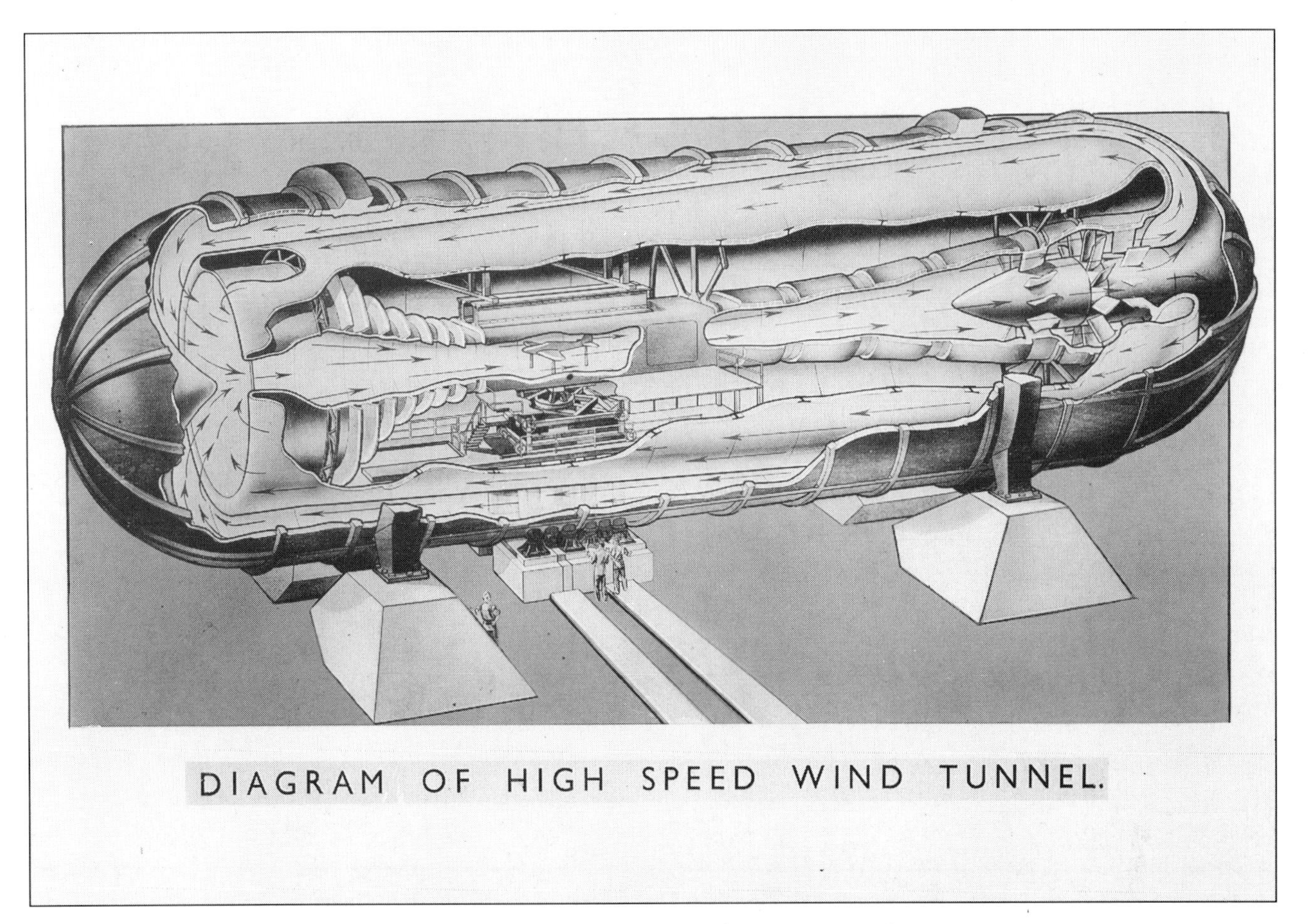

Figure 25. The RAE High Speed Tunnel, completed in 1942. [DRA Crown Copyright]

Figure 26. Hawker Typhoon model in the working section of the RAE High Speed Tunnel in 1942. [RAE Crown Copyright]

Figure 27. Sqdn Ldr Martindale's Spitfire Mk XI, EN 409, on Farnborough Airfield — minus its propeller and reduction gear, following a high speed test dive to a Mach Number of 0.91 on 27 April 1944. The brilliant reflection along the length of the fuselage is not the result of poor photography, but is due to oil, lost from the damaged engine, covering the aircraft from nose to tail. [RAE Crown Copyright]

Figure 28. Spitfire Mk 21, LA 188, used in RAE high Mach Number Research. [RAE Crown Copyright]

Figure 29. Spitfire memorial presentation in the Farnborough Officers' Mess garden in 1950. Facing camera and looking at the bronze model is Spitfire chief designer Joe Smith, successor to Reginald Mitchell; Jeffrey Quill, Supermarine chief test pilot, is intent on reading the plaque on the model mounting. Also present is J E Serby of the wartime headquarter's branch responsible for Spitfire Research & Development contracts and Group Captain Wheeler, CO of Experimental Flying, RAE. [RAE Crown Copyright]

Figure 30. Aerodynamics Flight Pilots May 1948. Rear row: Flt Lt J S R Muller Rowland, DSO, DFC; Lt R Mancus; Flt Lt C Adams; Flt Flt Lt G Genders, AFC, DFM; Fg Off J Lawrence (Flight Engineer). Front row: Flt Lt R V Ellis; Lt Cmdr E M Brown, OBE, DSC, AFC; Sqdn Sqdn Ldr R Whittome, OBE, DFC. [RAE Crown Copyright]

Figure 31. Captured Heinkel He 177 A5 photographed at RAE, Farnborough on 12 September 1944. [RAE Crown Copyright]

Figure 32. The de Havilland Mosquito, an outstanding wartime aircraft. RAE Mosquito Mk 6 RF 830 broke up in flight on 23 August 1945 catapaulting the crew through the cockpit roof. Flt Lt Brooks was able to use his parachute, but scientist/test observer 'Henry' Becker lost his life. [RAE Crown Copyright]

POST WAR ESCAPES

On 23 August 1945, people living by the Hog's Back near Farnham, Surrey, heard a sound in the sky similar to an explosion, followed by that of engines overspeeding. The noise was so unusual that many people looked up in the sky for the cause. Shortly afterward, wreckage fell out of the cloud, and from one of the objects a parachute was seen to stream close to the ground.

The aircraft was a de Havilland Mosquito, an outstanding wartime aircraft constructed almost entirely of laminated wood, flown by Aero Flight Division of the RAE, to investigate and alleviate aero-elastic problems at high speed. It had taken off earlier to test experimental tabs fitted to the elevator to restrict the 'g' loads which could be applied to the aircraft during flight manoeuvres. In a high speed pull-out manoeuvre, under increasing 'g', if a Mosquito pilot pulled the control column further back the stick force per 'g' reduced. There was, therefore, a danger of pilot over-control, leading to heavy 'g' loads and possible structural failure. The tabs were an attempt to alleviate this danger.

The test aircraft was flown by Flt Lt Clive Brooks, with aerodynamicist Mr 'Henry' Becker as test observer. On the last test run at 330 knots the 'stick' was torn from the pilot's grasp by the onset of elevator flutter, and the Mosquito went into a dive shaking violently. Then came the loud crack of a major structural failure, and the aircraft entered a vicious bunt which caused it to break up, catapulting the two crew, who were in the process of releasing their seat straps, prior to baling out, through the cockpit roof.

Brooks was wearing a seat-type parachute and recovered consciousness from a 'red out'* a few thousand feet above ground to stream his parachute. The rapidity of the break-up was such that Becker unfortunately did not have time to clip on his parachute properly, as it had been in a stowage, and his body was found near the wreckage. [Figure 32]

One consequence of this accident was that test observers, who were often moving around in the larger aircraft to set up test equipment, were issued with back-type parachutes to be worn in the air at all times.

The 1950s were the years of continuous development of the Avro Vulcan, Handley Page Victor, and Vickers Valiant V bombers, Britain's deterrent force of the time. The RAE had its own V bomber flight.

The special weapons, systems, and electronic test equipment carried by a Valiant of the RAE V Bomber Flight placed a heavy demand on the aircraft's electrical system. On 11 May 1956, Valiant WP 202, suffered a major in-flight electrical failure which affected its flight controls. The four-man crew remained on board, attempting to rectify the failure, while the senior pilot, Sqdn Ldr K Orman, struggled with the controls, finally crash landing, but managing to avoid housing, near Southwick, Sussex. No inhabitants were seriously hurt. At the last moment at a height of 150ft, the co-pilot, Flt Lt C D Preece was ordered to eject, just before the bomber hit the ground and exploded in an open space. Sadly the pilot and rear crew members, Flt Lt K E Evans and test observer Mr A R Knight died in the crash.

This was RAE's first live ejection. Flt Lt Preece showed his gratitude to Ivo Newman, who serviced and packed his parachute assembly, by presenting him with a traditional inscribed pewter tankard.

Considerable effort went into investigating the possible causes of this failure — then a near repeat of the accident occurred on Valiant WP 203 flying from RAE on 26 September 1957. Three of the rear-crew members, Flt Lt Labelle, Flt Lt Barker and Flt Lt Brooks who lacked ejection seats in the V bombers, were ordered to bale out using static line operated GQ Parachute Co back type assemblies. The two pilots, one of whom was Flt Lt Preece then flew the aircraft with great difficulty back to the RAE. In saving the aircraft they allowed a full investigation of the cause of the failure to be made. [Figure 34]

Caterpillar No 26, Flt Lt G G Davies, was on No 20 Course at the Empire Test Pilots School (ETPS) based at Farnborough, when on 13 October 1961 he ejected from a Hawker Hunter F4, XF 940, on approach to the airfield following a total fuel supply failure. Surprisingly, the aircraft landed itself virtually intact on Tweseldown racecourse, just to the West of the airfield. [Figure 37]

Flt Lt B Gartner, RCAF was also on a training course at the ETPS when he took off, on 16 July 1964, in a Supermarine Scimitar F1 naval aircraft on an exercise to investigate the aircraft's lift boundaries at high Mach numbers. At about Mach 1.3, over the English Channel, he encountered aerodynamic buffet followed by pitch-up of the aircraft and a violent undemanded manoeuvre which left the Scimitar with little electrical supplies and the engines in a condition where they could not be re-started. He ejected near the coast at a low level, parachuting into the sea some 200 yards from the beach at West Wittering, Sussex, whereupon holiday-makers swam out to help him ashore unhurt. The pilot was to comment that this was the most hazardous part of the whole ejection exercise. The aircraft hit the sea and exploded one half mile off shore.

---

* Under negative 'g' conditions, as in a bunt, blood supply to the brain is pooled and temporary unconsciousness can result, with the eyes 'seeing a red out'.

During the descent, the ejection seat was suspended below Flt Lt Gartner at the end of the leg restraint cords, the loops being locked onto the parachute lower attachment lugs. When the seat hit the water, the cords released. Immediately after this incident, leg restraint cords were re-routed to prevent a recurrence.

On 10 August 1977, Anne Burns, a member of the RAE Gliding Club, was flying a Nimbus sailplane in cloud conditions over Andover when there was a loud bang, the stick became free, and control was lost in a steep dive. She eventually had to bale out at 3,000 ft and landed in the branches of a sycamore tree 10 ft above the ground. It was her first parachute jump, at the age of 61.

Anne Burns was better known for her work over the years in the Structures Department, RAE on aircraft loads in clear air turbulence. Also for her flight test work in 1954, when the RAE was charged by the then Prime Minister, Winston Churchill, with making an urgent investigation into the cause of the tragic loss in January and April 1954 of two de Havilland Comet airliners with all on board, whilst on scheduled airline flights.

As one facet of these investigations, a Comet flew from Farnborough instrumented to measure structural stresses in flight during the climb to altitude. Anne Burns was a test observer on these flights, and was later awarded the Queen's Commendation for Valuable Service in the Air for her work.

Because of the unknown dangers that might be expected during the investigations of the Comet accidents, all the crew and scientists were issued with back type parachutes fitted with a Barometric Power Unit (BPU). During climb to altitude, just above BPU height setting, the parachute rip cords were pulled thereby arming the BPU, with the parachute opening sequence being unaffected. If a catastrophe occurred at altitude in the form of a complete breakup of the aircraft, crew and scientists would hopefully be thrown clear. Whether conscious or unconscious, when they had descended to the BPU preset operating altitude, the parachute would automatically open.

The overall RAE investigation was to show conclusively that the cause of the Comet accidents was a catastrophic metal fatigue/stress failure of the aircraft pressure cabin at altitude. Pressure cabin failure was first demonstrated in repeated pressure tests on the cabin of early production Comet G-ALYU, in a special 'water tank' at RAE, which showed that after a total of 3060 pressure cycles, stress/fatigue cracks, commencing at the corners of cabin cut outs for windows and aerials, led to failure of the structure. This mode of failure was fully confirmed when part of the pressure cabin of Comet G-ALYP was later recovered from the sea bed off the island of Elba in the Mediterranean. [Figure 36]

The Hawker Hunter T 12 which features in entries 29 and 30 on the RAE Caterpillar's board, was on Avionics Flight experimental 'fly by wire' aircraft used to investigate various methods of electrical signalling flying control and different forms of flight control laws. These were fed into the electrical signalling system by an 'on board' flight control computer.

The Hunter continued the work of the pioneer 'fly by wire' Avro 707C delta-wing research aircraft which had been fitted with an electrical signalling and manoeuvre demand control system and flown at the RAE in the late 1950s.

The Avro 707C led the way in the development of electrical signalling flight control systems, now familiar in aircraft. In the twin-seat aircraft, one pilot flew the aircraft using the experimental control system with flying controls operated by electrical signals initiated by the pilot's 'stick' and sent via wiring and an onboard computer, to flying control actuators. The second pilot could revert to conventional controls in the event of an emergency in the experimental system. [Figure 35]

On 17 March 1982, the Avro 707C's successor, Hunter T 12, XE 531, was taking off from Farnborough, piloted by Flt Lt R W Sears in company with co-pilot Mr A J Leng from the Brough Division of British Aerospace. The engine failed and burst during take-off with the aircraft only 10ft above the ground, and this severed the rear fuselage. With seconds to spare, both crew members ejected, Mr Leng drifting on his parachute through the fireball of the crash. [Figure 38]

The survival of the two crew members at such low altitude was further dramatic proof of the reliability of Martin Baker ejection seats, and of the advances made in aircrew escape systems since those early days when Farnborough pioneers such as Cody, Busk, and Goodden had no choice but to stay with their aircraft in a flight emergency.

The escape from the Hunter provided the last entry on the RAE Caterpillars list. No more names appeared before the last research aircraft left Farnborough on 24 March 1994, leaving the airfield hangars, once full of activity, silent and still. These aircraft were transferred to Boscombe Down, Wiltshire as was the RAE Caterpillar's list. [Figure 40]

In compiling this account of the RAE Caterpillars, and the small part of the Establishment's overall research effort linked to these parachute escapes, the work of many RAE departments has not been mentioned. Instrument and Photographic, Naval Aircraft, Armament, Radio, Structural and Mechanical Departments and their Flights were equally active over the years with many very successful research programmes. These departments also had aircraft and aircrew losses during their research work, but no parachute escapes are recorded.

Several vital threads seem to run through this

account of just some of the flying from Farnborough over the years. These are the importance of continuity in aircraft research work and in developing special test facilities, together with the need for close liaison between flight test, and experimental and theoretical work in the technical departments. It must be hoped that these pointers from the past are not lost sight of during the fundamental changes taking place with the re-organisation of the Defence Research Establishments into Agencies.

The Defence Research Agency plan to vacate the historic 'Factory' site in 1996 and move to new purpose-built accommodation in the vicinity of Ball Hill on the Western side of the airfield. The 'Factory' site will be returned to the Ministry of Defence for disposal. Its future use is as yet undecided and will depend to a large extent on the outcome of current deliberations by the local Authority. [Figure 39]

Figure 33. de Havilland 108 tailless research aircraft, VW 120, in which RAE test pilot Sqdn Ldr J S R Muller Rowland, DSO, DFC, lost his life on 15 February 1950. [via Aeroplane Monthly]

Figure 34. Vickers Valiant bomber WB 215. Valiant B1s, WP 202 and WP 203, flying from RAE, increased membership of the Caterpillar Club by four in 1956 and 1957. [RAE Crown Copyright]

Figure 35. 'Fly by wire' Avro 707C research aircraft. [DRA Crown Copyright]

Figure 36. Part of the wreckage of the pressure cabin of Comet G-ALYP which fell into the Mediterranean on 10 January 1954, showing stress/fatique cracks originating from the corners of cabin cut-outs (required for directional aerials). [RAE Crown Copyright]

Figure 37. Hunter F4, XF 940, photographed in 1959, from which Flt Lt Davies safely ejected on the approach to Farnborough airfield on 13 October 1961. [via Aeroplane Monthly]

Figure 38. Hunter T 12 from which Flt Lt Sears and A J Leng successfully ejected when the engine failed on take-off severing the rear fuselage. [RAE Crown Copyright].

Figure 39. Aerial view of the RAE 'Factory' site in July 1977. The 24ft wind tunnel can be recognised by its clock face high up on the building, providing a well-known local landmark. [RAE Crown Copyright]

Figure 40. Fly past over Farnborough Airfield of the last research aircraft to leave for Boscombe Down, Wiltshire on 24 March 1994. [DRA Crown Copyright]

ACKNOWLEDGEMENTS

Many of the photographs in this book have been kindly supplied by the Defence Research Agency and are Crown Copyright. They are reproduced with the permission of the Controller of Her Majesty's Stationery Office.

Particular thanks are due to Captain E M Brown, RN for providing a much appreciated Foreword, to Mr Brian Kervell, Curator of the RAE/DRA Museum 1982-1994, for general assistance and advice freely given and to Wg Cmdr D R Collier Webb, RAF Retd, of MOD (PE) Flight Safety, for information used to verify some of the escape stories.

Mention must also be made of Ivo Newman, ex-RAE Parachute R & D Section, who processed the manuscript of this book with an expertise equal to that of his experimental parachute work. He also provided additional information on three of the escapes described in this book. Three members of 'Farnborough's Caterpillars' have particular reason to be grateful to Ivo Newman, as he serviced and packed their assemblies whilst working in the Survival Equipment Section.

Very special thanks are extended to RAE colleague Bob Rose, who in retirement founded Footmark Publications, and whose wholehearted support and encouragement enabled this book to be produced.

The book is based on an article by the Author which first appeared in the January and February 1994 issues of Aeroplane Monthly. Thanks are also due to the Editor, Mr Richard Riding, and to Mr Philip Jarrett and Group Captain Peter Hearn for providing a number of the photographs used.

BIBLIOGRAPHY

Readers interested in parachutes, emergency escapes from aircraft and flight testing could find further information from the following publications:

The Sky People — a history of parachuting by Group Captain Peter Hearn, Airlife, 1990

Sky High Irvin — the story of a parachute pioneer by Group Captain Peter Hearn, Hale, 1983

Wings on my Sleeve by Captain Eric Brown, RN, Airlife, 1978

Testing for Combat by Captain Eric Brown, RN, Airlife, 1994

APPENDIX

The Caterpiller Club

(by courtesy of Irvin Aerospace)

A Brief History

This unique and exclusive club was formed in 1922 by Leslie L Irvin and its membership is limited to those people, no matter what nationality, race, creed or sex, whose lives have been saved in an emergency by an Irvin designed or manufactured parachute. The name 'CATERPILLAR' was chosen by Leslie Irvin himself in conjunction with Lieutenants Harris and Tyndall of the USAAC, who were in fact the first two people to owe their lives to an Irvin parachute. There were two reasons for the choice of the club's name; the silken threads from which parachutes of the time were woven were produced by the carerpillar, and also the caterpillar lets itself down to earth by a silken thread it has spun. These facts also gave the club its slogan 'Life depends on a silken thread'. Each member, on being accepted into the club, is presented with a membership card, and also a gold pin in the shape of a caterpillar on the back of which is engraved the name and rank of the member.

In the first year there were just two members, Harris and Tyndall, mentioned above, but by the outbreak of the Second World War in 1939 the total membership was approximately 4000. The UK roll has now grown to a staggering 32,020. Obviously a large proportion of this total represents Service personnel who have been forced to bale out over enemy territory only to become captured, and the stack of Prisoner of War Cards that arrived every day during the Second world War was between 100 and 150. An individual file for most members is maintained, and some of the contents on the back of these Prisoner of War Cards make interesting reading.

Typical examples are:

"Dear Sir, will you please enrol me as a Member of the Caterpillar Club. I baled out over Holland on August 15th from a blazing kite and made a wizard landing."

"God bless you Brother Leslie on behalf of my wife and children, as yet unknown."

"Dear Leslie, I'd like to thank you for the sweetest moments in all my life, when my parachute opened and I realised I was not going to die. Your 'chutes are so good I am going to name my son (when I have one) Irvin as it was due to one in particular that I am alive enough to woo, marry and get me a son."

Many now famous names appear on the Membership List such as Tom Campbell Black, Geoffrey de Havilland, John Cunningham of Comet fame, Wing Commander Douglas Bader and Jimmy Doolittle, who has saved his life by an Irvin parachute three times.

POSTSCRIPT

I have known Dick Dennis, the author of 'Farnborough's Caterpillars' for many years. We were colleagues from the early 40s to the early 60s in Aero Flight Division, RAE — first at Farnborough and then at Bedford. In 1962 Dick moved to the Aircraft Torpedo Development Unit based at Culdrose, Cornwall, before going to Headquarters. Finally our paths converged again at Farnborough when he became Head of Parachute Research Section and I was a member of Helicopter Division.

I well remember much of the high speed flight research described by Dick — particularly the wartime high speed dives on Spitfires and early post-war transonic flight tests.

Dick Dennis became a member of the Caterpillar Club whilst at RAE Bedford; thus his name is not inscribed on the wallboard of Farnborough's Caterpillars. This is unfortunate as it would have been unique in the annals of RAE escapes.

He made an unusual escape from a large barrage balloon which had been inadvertently wound above 5000ft altitude and thus came free from its ground winch. The balloon then drifted across RAE Larkhill Range on Salisbury Plain, rapidly gaining height with Dick and his colleague Roger Austin suspended below in the balloon carriage.

This occurred on 30 April 1958, when they were engaged in free flight spinning tests on a model of the Bristol 188 research aircraft. This involved dropping a model from the balloon carriage at a planned 5000ft altitude. The model controls were timed to operate to cause the model first to enter and then attempt recovery from the spin.

When they realised they were no longer tethered to the ground, one of the pair is reputed to have said: "Do you know, I think they have let us go!" They both used their rip-cord operated parachutes to escape at an altitude of about 10,000 ft, Roger going first. When he was safely on his parachute, Dick clearly heard him shouting, "Come on in, it's your turn!" Both landed on the northern edge of the impact area of the military West Down artillery range; the Range Controller fortunately managed to stop the guns from firing into the area a few minutes before they safely landed.

There was unfortunately a sad sequel to this escape; Roger Austin was killed shortly afterward in a car accident when returning from his honeymoon.

I share the author's concern that some 80 years of flight research at Farnborough has ceased with so little done to mark this important phase of aviation history. Thus I think that 'Farnborough's Caterpillars' will help to set the record straight. It will be enjoyed by many who took part in RAE's aeronautical past and be a valuable record for those who know little of this, but wish to find out more.

Farnborough Air Sciences Trust has been formed by a group of aviation enthusiasts. The Trust's aims include the saving of a large part of the historic Main Factory Site from possible demolition; in particular to save the magnificent wind tunnels, and to reconstruct a historic airship shed from components located in various redundant buildings. It is hoped in time to secure the return of artefacts of the now disbanded RAE Museum and possibly some of the Cody artefacts on loan from the Drachen Foundation and other successful bidders at the Cody Archive auction. These could be included in a museum, housed in the 24ft wind tunnel, to record Farnborough's achievements in aeronautical research; also perhaps to display some of the current work of the Defence Research Agency at Farnborough.

The author and myself as publisher, fully support the aims of the Farnborough Air Sciences Trust (FAST) and to this end we will donate half the proceeds from the sale of 'Farnborough's Caterpillars' to FAST.

Bob Rose, Footmark Publications,
Fleet, April 1996

INDEX